THE HOLE IN THE TREE

A 1961 Selection of the
WEEKLY READER
Children's Book Club
Education Center • Columbus 16, Ohio

THE HOLE IN THE TREE

story and pictures

by JEAN GEORGE

E. P. DUTTON & CO., INC. PUBLISHERS

WEEKLY READER
Children's Book Club
Edition, 1961

LIBRARY OF CONGRESS CATALOG CARD NO.: 57-5348

To
TWIG,
a little girl
who likes holes
in trees

THE HOLE IN THE TREE

THE HOLE IN THE TREE

The apple tree in the farmyard was growing old. For many years it had flowered and borne fruit. It was twisted and bent, but for all its years it was still firm and green.

The lowest limbs of the apple tree dipped to the ground. When the leaves covered the branches there was a secret room under the tree. Into the secret room came mice and baby robins to hide from the fox and the farmer. Squirrels came into the room to store their nuts, and raccoons brought ears of corn under the tree to picnic.

Scot and Paula Gordon came to the secret room, too. They liked to be where nobody could see them.

One dry, hot summer morning something exciting happened to the tree. It was a very small excitement.

Scot was in the secret room digging a hole for his treasure box, when a flight of bark beetles flew by. One beetle alighted on his shoulder. Scot puffed up his cheeks and blew so hard that the beetle tumbled through the air and landed on the trunk of the tree. The bark beetle folded her wings neatly on her back and started climbing the wrinkled bark.

Scot hummed and dug deeper into the earth. He did not notice the bark beetle stop and bite into the bark.

This tiny beetle bite was the beginning of the hole in the tree.

The beetle chewed through the bark into the white, moist sapwood. She was not a good beetle to have in a tree, for she brought with her a fungus disease that would kill the tree.

Soon the bark beetle had tunneled a straight avenue in which to lay her eggs. Then she rested.

Into the bark beetle's hole came another beetle, the wood borer. She tunneled deeper into the tree to lay her eggs.

The hole in the tree was so small that a caterpillar walked past it without seeing it.

Suddenly there was a rat-a-tat-tat. Old Stonehead, the downy woodpecker, had found the beetle hole. He drilled so fast that it seemed his head would fly off as he bored through the bark beetle's hole into the wood borer's gallery. His tongue had forked hooks at its end, and when he found the worms of the wood borer, he lifted them from the hole as neatly as a fox plucks grapes.

When old Stonehead had finished, the hole in the tree was bigger.

The hole in the tree was now **as big as a housefly**. It still seemed small, but to something not much bigger than a housefly, such a hole could be a home.

One day during corn-on-the-cob season, Paula was in the secret room building a house of twigs for a beetle she liked. She heard a buzz near her head and sat quite still as a large carpenter bee streaked past. The big black bee lowered all six of her legs and came to rest on the trunk of the apple tree. Slowly she climbed the tree to search for a hole. She was ready to lay her **eggs**.

The large carpenter bee came to the hole in the tree. It was just what she wanted, except that it was too small. She began to bite the hole bigger and bigger with her strong jaws. She could bite the fungus-rotted wood as easily as Paula could bite apples.

At the end of the day the hole in the tree was as big as the head of a thumb tack. And inside the hole the carpenter bee was chewing her tunnel downward. She swept out the bites with her brushes.

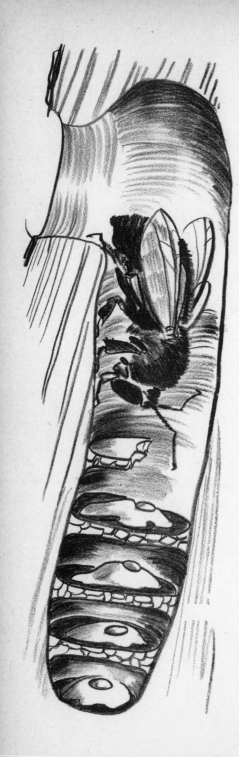

When the carpenter bee had chewed a tunnel almost as long as Paula's foot, she gathered pollen and nectar, and placed them at the bottom of the tunnel. She laid an egg on the sweet pile.

Then she made a lid over the egg with scraps of wood mixed with her saliva. The lid sealed the egg into the tree.

She placed more pollen and honey on the lid and laid another egg. She covered this with a second lid.

She laid eggs and made lids until she came to the bend in the tunnel. Here she rested and waited for her babies to hatch.

The bee eggs hatched about the time that the apples turned red. The egg at the bottom of the tunnel hatched first. Out squirmed a larva that looked like a worm. The larva

ate its pollen and honey and gradually changed into a pupa that looked like a little bee wrapped in swaddling clothes. Inside the covering miracles were taking place, and one day the wrapping split and out came a perfect little carpenter bee. It tore down the lid above it and found another bee coming out of its pupa case. Together they tore down the next lid, and found a third pupa.

Bee by bee, lid by lid, ten little **car**-penter bees emerged. They all tore down the last lid and there was their mother. She helped them brush the tunnel clean. Then they followed her into the meadow.

When night came she led them back to the hole in the tree.

One night the bees went into the hole and did not come out the next morning. They did not come out for many months. It was winter. The fungus stopped growing and the bees became so cold they could not move their feet or wings.

When the air grew warm with the coming of spring, the bees wiggled their legs and then their wings. The fungus began to grow again. One day the bees flew out of the hole in the tree to find new homes. One little bee circled around and came back to the apple tree.

But a hole in a tree is not an easy thing to keep.

When the bee was out eating one day, Deelet, the black-capped chickadee, came to the apple tree. She needed a hole in which to lay eggs and raise her baby birds.

She saw the bee-hole. It was too small, but she pecked it any-way. The rotted wood crumbled as Deelet pounded.

She dug and chipped and pecked and hammered. Wood chips fell like flower petals. She worked for thirty minutes without stopping, and when she was tired, Black-cap, her mate, took her place at the hole.

When the bee returned she found a big hole where her little hole had been. She buzzed away.

By dusk the hole in the tree was as big as a golf ball and almost a chickadee deep.

Seven days later, and seven finger-lengths deeper in the apple tree, sat Deelet, the chickadee. In her bill was a puff of rabbit fur. She pressed it into the nest she had woven at the bottom of the hole.

Two days later she laid a tiny speckled egg. It was no bigger than a marble. Every morning she laid another egg until there were seven.

After she had laid the seventh egg she settled down to heat the eggs with her warm breast. The warmth was the magic that would change the yolk and albumin in the eggs into tiny chickadees.

Incubation time is a quiet time for birds, and Black-cap sang his "hi-sweetie" song only in the pink hours of dawn.

The apple blossoms opened, the leaves came out, while deep in the dark hole Deelet sat on her eggs.

Twelve days later there were seven pea-sized chickadees in the hole in the tree, and on that day Paula and Scot saw that the apple leaves were full. They remembered the secret room and crawled under the branches.

Small voices spoke from the tree. Paula put her ear to the trunk and listened. The apple tree was peeping. At this moment Black-cap arrived at the hole with a billful of nestling food. He slipped into the darkness and somebody gobbled and chirped. Black-cap popped to the door, looked about and flew away. Then Deelet arrived with food.

"A chickadee nest!" whispered Scot. By sitting very still Paula and Scot were able to watch the chickadees feed their young.

One day a downy-headed chickadee sat in the doorway. He was pushed from behind. He flapped his wings and skidded onto a nearby twig. Where he had been sat another puff of chickadee. By push and flip, seven baby chickadees came out of the hole in the tree until it was empty. Paula and Scot watched them fly into the treetops.

Now the apple tree was silent. The children built roads and houses under the limbs and forgot the hole in the tree. A deserted hole is so empty.

The October moon was climbing the sky when a frightened little deer mouse darted out of the field and into the secret room. Above her swooped a screech owl, his sharp talons swinging low above her head. Perrie, the deer mouse, spiraled up the tree and by good fortune ran right into the hole. She tumbled down and bounced softly into the chickadee's nest.

The owl clicked his beak and flew on. Perrie, as safe as a

mouse could be, rearranged the bowl of the chickadee nest into the hollow ball of a mouse nest. She set up housekeeping in the hole in the tree.

Many days later when Scot was gathering apples, the tree spoke to him again. He watched to see if a chickadee would fly out, but none appeared. It was almost bedtime before he saw, to his surprise, five baby mice come down the tree with their mother and run along their mouse-avenue to the field for seeds.

That night when he and Paula were alone, he told her of the new secret in the hole in the tree.

Paula and Scot saved cheese from their lunch and put it under the apple tree; but Perrie and her babies never found it. They had already left.

The dawn of that morning, old Stonehead, the downy woodpecker, had returned to the apple tree to hunt. He found the hole and with a bang and a tat-a-tat-tat, frightened the mouse family out of the nest.

Stonehead cleaned out the grass and rabbit fur, chipped the bottom of the hole larger, to make space for his stiff tail, and fitted himself into the hole in the tree. The clean dry walls hugged him like a blanket. He announced with a "yak" that the hole was his new night roost, and then went out to eat.

When the sun was at ten minutes past five, Stonehead went back to his hole and plunged down in it. As soon as his body heated the little bedroom, he fell asleep.

At midnight a mouse face appeared at the doorway and vanished. Perrie had come back, smelled woodpecker in her hole, and had gone to the field to live under a stone.

All through the winter Stonehead roosted in the hole in the tree. He returned to it earlier each night; eight minutes past five, six minutes past five, four minutes past five, according to the setting of the sun. When the **air** was freezing cold he would come back to the hole during the day to warm his feet.

One winter twilight when the snow was falling, Stonehead came home earlier than usual. It was too cold and nasty to stay out. He yaked, "goodnight," and went to bed.

Stonehead yaked again and tumbled out. Someone was in his bed! Stonehead regained his balance and peered cautiously into the hole. He saw the shining right eye of Pickit, the white-breasted nuthatch.

Feathers flew and bills clashed as the furious woodpecker and

the angry nuthatch fought for the hole in the tree. In a few minutes a screaming bird flew off into the cold. Deep in the hole sat the other bird, fussing and smoothing his feathers.

The bird in the hole was

Stonehead, the victorious downy woodpecker.

One cool yellow dawn Stonehead was awakened by the cry, "peeek!" The announcement upset him. He lifted his feathers and jabbed at the wooden walls, and made up his mind not to come out of the hole in the tree. If he did he knew he would lose his hole.

As he waited and fussed, he grew hungrier and hungrier. Finally, he could hide no longer. Out he came.

Before Stonehead could call, "goodmorning," he was

hit on the head by the wing of Bristles, the hairy woodpecker. Bristles looked just like Stonehead, only he was twice as big and much meaner. Before Stonehead had reached the elm tree, Bristles was chopping away at the hole in the tree. Stonehead knew it was hopeless to fight Bristles. He went down to the woods and did not come back.

Bristles made the hole bigger and bigger, then he announced to the farmyard that he, Bristles, the hairy woodpecker, was king of the hole in the tree.

But Bristles did not keep the hole in the tree very long. It was spring and many birds and animals wanted a hole.

The flying squirrels took it from Bristles when he stayed out late one evening.

The house sparrows fussed and pecked until they got it from the flying squirrels, and the starlings took it from the house sparrows.

The starlings filled it with sticks and string and paper to make a nest that looked more like a trash can than a home. By the time they had stuffed it with everything they could pick up, it was too small for them. They deserted it; and when Rufo, the crested flycatcher, arrived in the yard, he was glad for any hole at all. He threw out the litter and used the hole in the tree until he could find one in the forest.

When Rufo left, nobody came to the hole in the tree for days. By this time almost everyone who wanted a hole had one.

The starlings, the sparrows, the flying squirrels, the crested flycatcher, all had holes. Only one little bird who very much needed a hole, didn't have one. She was Sky, the bluebird.

Sky was sitting timidly above the hole in the tree looking at it tenderly. She was afraid to go near it, for Paula was under the tree stringing apple blossoms on a thread.

Sky needed the hole for her second nest of the season. She gathered courage, flew over Paula's head, and looked into the hole. She slipped in, pushed down to the dry woody bottom, and chirped softly.

Paula chirped softly too. "A bluebird's nest!"

Sky and her mate built their nest in the hole in the tree. The day before Sky laid her first egg, Bursto, the house wren, discovered the hole. No one was home. He bubbled his fountain of song, then gathered sticks and thrust them into the bluebird's nest. Bursto had a habit of putting sticks in every hole he could find.

Sky came back to her nest late in the day to find it stuffed with Bursto's presents. Clicking and scolding she threw them out, then hid behind the tree trunk.

There was an explosion of wren song below her. Bursto

came to her door with another stick. Sky **was ar**ound the tree and hitting him with her wing before he could move. Undaunted, the wren carried his stick to the clothesline and thrust it in a hole in a sock.

When Sky had laid her fifth and last egg she could still hear Bursto in the garden announcing to the world that he had just put another stick in a hole.

The bluebird eggs hatched and the pot-bellied babies grew into beautiful little nestlings. When Scot was helping with the second mowing of the hay crop, the nestlings came out of the hole in the tree.

Scot and Paula found them scattered on the ground under the tree. Sky and her mate were frantically calling them into the safety of the limbs. The children tried to catch them and put them in the tree, but the little bluebirds needed no help. They

hopped and fluttered onto the apple tree limbs; and the next morning they were gone.

The hole in the tree was quiet again; but not empty. Deep in the lining of the bluebird's nest were ants, fleas, flies, beetles and their larvae.

Some of the insects were cleaning up the bluebird's nest. Others, who fed on birds, were waiting for them to return.

Sky came back to the apple tree to see if her nest could be used for a third brood. She might have suffered the bites of the insects were it not for the fact that Yellow-shaft, the flicker, had got there first.

He was at the hole in the tree listening to the smallest of sounds — larvae moving in the dry lining of the nest inside.

He chopped, listened, chopped; and finally made the hole so big he could get his head in. He jabbed his beak into the nest lining and speared the larvae. When Yellow-shaft flew off, the hole in the tree was as big as a baseball.

That evening the hole in the tree had a new owner. It wasn't a bird; it wasn't an insect; it wasn't a wild animal. It was Scot.

He had crawled under the limbs to finish a tunnel, and noticed the wood chips under the tree, and a big hole where the little hole had been.

Then he did what everybody else who had found the hole in the tree had done. He tried it for size. His hand could reach

the woody bottom! With a shouted "wow," Scot announced to
the farmyard that he now claimed the hole in the tree.

He took from his pocket a big English penny, a piece of string,
and a marble. He placed them at the bottom of the hole. He
patted the bark, mumbled a secret word; and became king of
the hole in the tree.

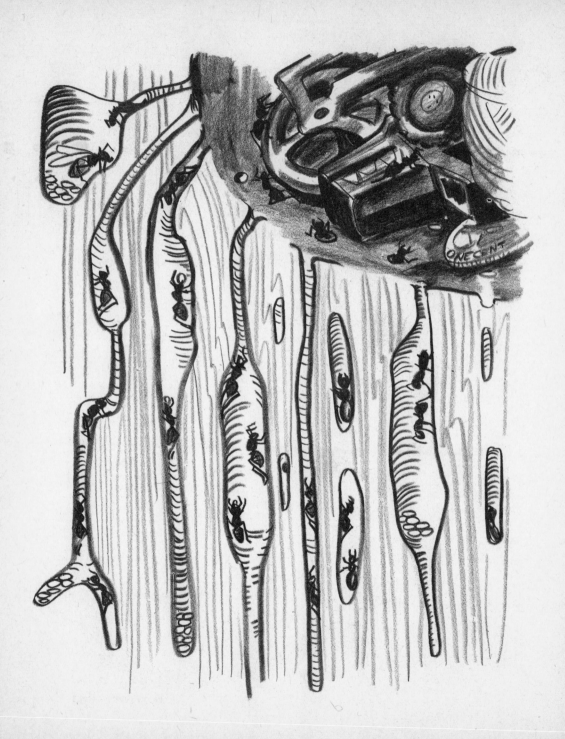

Scot was able to claim the hole in the tree for only three brief weeks. Although his treasure pile mounted, and he was bigger and stronger than anyone else who had owned the hole, still he was unable to keep it. He was defeated by a tiny enemy.

A queen carpenter ant walked up the tree one day, and into the hole. She crawled over the mound of string and marbles and dug a tidy hole into the rotted wood at the bottom of the cavity. Here she laid many eggs. They hatched into worker ants and made hundreds of tunnels in the tree. In some of the tunnels the queen laid more eggs. They hatched and made more tunnels and the queen laid more eggs. Presently there were enough carpenter ants to attack almost anything that came to the hole in the tree.

One windy September day, Scot reached into the hole for his kite string. Three carpenter ants attacked him. Many more raced to bite the intruder. Scot pulled his arm out swiftly, and sat down to plan a war with the ants.

The battle never came about.

Early the next morning an enormous bird came to the apple tree. He was old Giant Driller, the pileated woodpecker. He was flying to the big swamp forests at the edge of the farm, and he stopped in the farmyard to investigate the carpenter ants who were marching up and down the apple tree.

Old Giant Driller began to hammer at the tree. He sounded

like a wood chopper felling an oak. He cut a hole big enough for himself, flicked all the treasures out and finished off the carpenter ants.

Then he flew away, leaving the hole in the tree as big as Scot's head.

When Paula and Scot discovered the enormous hole, they could only wonder who had done it. Sadly Scot picked up his treasures and told Paula of his wonderful secret that now seemed to be everyone's.

"It's big enough for both of us," she said gayly, and reached in. "We can leave messages for each other here as well as treasures."

That night a water pistol, a broken doll, and a teacup lay in the bottom of the hole. There was also a note that read:

"Mommy is going to have a baby. I hope it's a girl. Paula."

Winter came to the land. The treasures and the note were forgotten.

In the dark of the night, someone went into the hole in the tree. She found the note, chewed it, fingered the water pistol and put the teacup on her nose. She hugged the doll; then Fumbles, the raccoon, fell asleep.

Fumbles awoke early to find it snowing. She didn't like snow, and she slipped back into the den to curl up around the doll, the teacup, and the pistol. She was fat and did not need to eat for many months. She had the driest hole on the farm. It had snug white walls, and loveliest of all — toys!

Fumbles closed her eyes and began her long winter sleep.

Many snowstorms and a spring thaw later, Fumbles was awakened by another raccoon. He was putting the teacup on his toe. She growled, recognized her mate, Mask, and went back to sleep.

At the end of March, Scot came to the hole in the tree to hide a rusty fox trap he had found. He reached in the hole.

"Fur!" he said aloud. "Who's hidden his Davy Crockett hat in my hole?" He ran and told Paula, and she decided they should write the person a note.

"Danger lurks here!" it read. They placed it on the Davy Crockett hat. The next day the note was gone but the hat wasn't.

"If we can't scare him, we'll make friends," said Paula, as she penciled another note.

"Who are you? Let's be friends."

The next day that note was gone. The hat remained. Scot and Paula sat down to talk over another plan.

"We'll just have to take the hat in the house, and the owner will have to knock at the door to get it," Scot was saying, as Fumbles looked out the hole to see what the commotion was.

"Of course!" Paula answered and stood up to get the hat. Boy and girl and raccoon stared at one another, all equally surprised. Fumbles retreated into her den, and as she did, she dropped a piece of paper she had been playing with. It read:

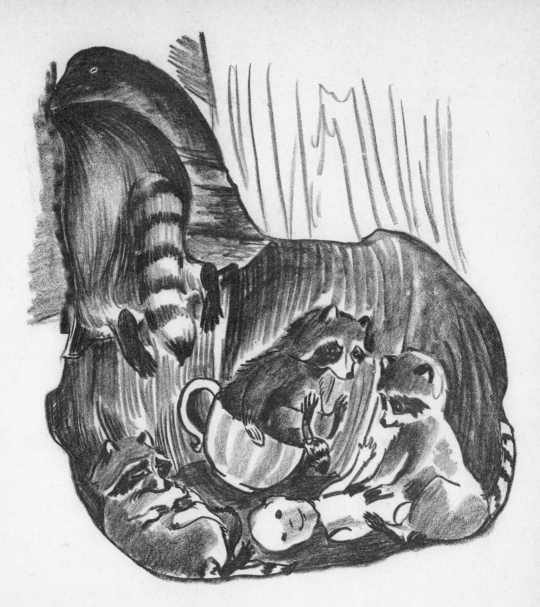

"Mommy   have baby.   Pa ."

Scot read the note and put his ear to the tree. Softly through
the woody walls came the chuttering sounds of baby raccoons.

From the porch of the house Mr. Gordon called: "Paula! Scot! We have a baby sister!"

A bark beetle alighted on Scot's shoulder. He brushed it away as he ran through the limbs of the old apple tree with Paula. The bark beetle did not see them running happily into the house.

It was climbing the wrinkled trunk looking for a good place
for a bark beetle to bite a hole in the tree.